STAR WARS

S0-CFD-981

CONTENTS

Pedigree®

ublished 2011. Pedigree Books Ltd, Beech Hill House, Walnut Gardens, Exeter, Devon EX4 4DH
ooks@pedigreegroup.co.uk | www.pedigreebooks.com

99

QUI-GON JINN

Qui-Gon Jinn is something of a maverick Jedi, although he is an experienced and wise Master. He was trained by Count Dooku, who went on to abandon the Jedi Order. However, Qui-Gon is loyal to the Jedi and is strongly connected to the living Force. He shows great care and concern for other living things, and is a fearsome warrior.

OBI-WAN KENOBI

Obi-Wan Kenobi is a young and dedicated Jedi Knight. Although he can be impatient, he is also a bold and agile warrior. As he grows older, he is becoming an extremely resourceful Jedi who his friends and colleagues trust absolutely. Obi-Wan's loyalty and kind heart are equal to his ingenuity and intelligence.

DARTH SIDIOUS

Darth Sidious is an evil Sith Lord who exists in the shadows and conceals his true identity. His ultimate aim is to destroy the Jedi Order and gain unlimited power. He is behind every plot and event that undermines the Republic, and his ambition is limitless.

DARTH MAUL

Darth Maul is a ruthless warrior who serves Darth Sidious with absolute obedience. His terrifying appearance reflects the darkness at his core, and he has been conditioned and trained as a heartless killer. He travels with death as a constant companion, and his delight in killing fits with his Sith background.

ANAKIN SKYWALKER

Anakin Skywalker is a loving and kind child who has no idea how special he really is. He possesses extraordinary Force skills and piloting abilities. He has only ever known a life of slavery, but he dreams of one day freeing all slaves and providing his mother with a peaceful, comfortable life.

SHMI SKYWALKER

Shmi Skywalker is Anakin's mother. She was sold into slavery as a young girl, and she works hard. Her master, Watto, is cruel and rough, but he does give her a tiny bit of independence. When she isn't busy working for him, he allows her to clean computer memory devices to earn a little money.

JAR JAR BINKS

Jar Jar Binks comes from a huge underwater city called Otoh Gunga. He is very kind and helpful, but he has a knack for getting into trouble and is very clumsy. His very trusting nature sometimes enables other people to take advantage of him.

QUEEN AMIDALA

The beautiful Queen Amidala is dedicated to the safety and peace of her home planet. She is a courageous young woman and a fiercely intelligent politician. She sometimes uses her handmaidens as decoys, dressing them as herself while she puts on their clothes.

WORD HUNTER

There are fifteen words hiding inside this grid, all connected with the events surrounding the discovery of Anakin Skywalker. Can you find them all? They may be written forwards, backwards, up, down or diagonally.

- [ ] BATTLE
- [ ] BONGO
- [ ] CORUSCANT
- [ ] DISGUISE
- [ ] DROIDS
- [ ] GUNGANS
- [ ] INVASION
- [ ] NABOO
- [ ] PROPHECY
- [ ] REPUBLIC
- [ ] SENATE
- [ ] SLAVES
- [ ] SPEEDER
- [ ] TATOOINE
- [ ] WATTO

C	I	N	C	I	D	U	I	E	T	U	E	R	O	S
I	Q	T	A	T	O	O	I	N	E	B	L	A	N	A
D	A	T	I	R	I	T	V	A	E	A	F	A	O	E
I	F	A	C	I	P	T	E	B	T	V	E	L	I	M
S	Q	T	U	E	R	A	I	O	O	Q	U	A	S	S
G	W	N	R	I	L	W	O	O	U	N	U	T	A	O
U	L	A	Q	O	D	D	U	I	E	T	G	L	V	R
I	O	C	Y	N	R	D	E	R	O	E	A	O	N	Y
S	P	S	T	Z	O	A	R	E	P	U	B	L	I	C
E	Q	U	U	L	I	E	I	E	R	S	E	D	E	E
L	E	R	B	P	D	O	U	T	R	I	L	I	Q	H
I	M	O	Q	E	S	E	V	A	L	S	L	A	A	P
Q	U	C	E	P	S	U	S	N	E	S	S	I	B	O
U	A	P	A	Q	O	N	S	E	L	T	T	A	B	R
L	S	N	A	G	N	U	G	S	I	L	L	A	C	P

THE PHANTOM
menace

The Trade Federation has blockaded the planet Naboo. Jedi Knights Qui-Gon Jinn and Obi-Wan Kenobi have been sent to negotiate. They don't know that Nute Gunray is acting under the orders of a Sith Lord, Darth Sidious.

Darth Sidious orders Gunray to kill the Jedi.

However, the Jedi destroy his droideka droids and escape to the planet's surface.

Queen Amidala of Naboo tries to contact Senator Palpatine on Coruscant, but the Trade Federation cuts all communications. That can only mean one thing – invasion!

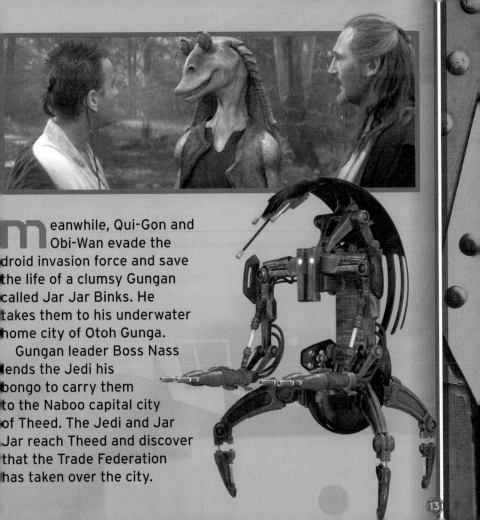

meanwhile, Qui-Gon and Obi-Wan evade the droid invasion force and save the life of a clumsy Gungan called Jar Jar Binks. He takes them to his underwater home city of Otoh Gunga.

Gungan leader Boss Nass lends the Jedi his bongo to carry them to the Naboo capital city of Theed. The Jedi and Jar Jar reach Theed and discover that the Trade Federation has taken over the city.

In the palace throne room, Nute Gunray tells Queen Amidala that her people will suffer unless she agrees to a treaty. As she and her handmaidens are led towards a prison camp, the Jedi are watching.

The Jedi attack the battle droids and rescue the Queen. Then they all escape in a Naboo spacecraft. They set a course for Coruscant, where the Queen hopes to persuade the Senate to condemn the Trade Federation invasion.

Darth Sidious orders his assistant, Darth Maul, to find the Queen. Meanwhile, the Naboo spacecraft needs a new hyperdrive generator, so the ship lands on the planet of Tatooine to refuel and get repairs. Qui-Gon takes Jar Jar, a droid called R2-D2 and a handmaiden named Padmé to the city of Mos Espa.

In a junk shop run by a Toydarian called Watto, they meet a young slave boy called Anakin Skywalker.

Watto will not accept Republican credits, and Qui-Gon has no money. They leave the shop, but Anakin bumps into them in the marketplace. When a sandstorm blows up, he offers them shelter in his home.

Qui-Gon meets Anakin's mother Shmi, and Anakin shows off the droid he has built – C-3PO. Anakin tells the newcomers about Podracing, a sport he loves. He is the only human who can do it.

nakin has a kind heart and wants to help his new friends. He offers to pilot his own Podracer in the next race. The prize money will pay for the parts Qui-Gon needs.

Watto agrees to let Anakin race. If the boy wins, he will keep the prize money minus the cost of the parts. If the boy loses, Watto will keep the Podracer.

CONTINUES PAGE 22

17

TEST YOUR JEDI SKILLS

PART 1

QUESTION 1

WHICH ANIMAL ARE YOU MOST LIKE?

a. Cheetah ☐
b. Dog ☐
c. Cat ☐

QUESTION 2

CAN YOU:

a. Touch your toes? ☐
b. Do a backflip? ☐
c. Do a handstand? ☐

QUESTION 3

YOUR FRIENDS COME TO YOU FOR:

a. Advice ☐
b. Fun ☐
c. Gossip ☐

QUESTION 4

HOW MANY PEOPLE DO YOU LOVE?

a. 1-4 ☐
b. 5-9 ☐
c. More than 10 ☐

ARE YOU READY TO BECOME A JEDI? THE JEDI COUNCIL REQUIRES YOU TO PASS CERTAIN TESTS TO PROVE THAT YOU ARE FIT FOR TRAINING. ANSWER THESE QUESTIONS TO DISCOVER IF YOU ARE SUITABLE FOR THE HONOUR OF BECOMING A JEDI.

QUESTION 5

YOU HAVE STOPPED TO HELP A STRANGER:

a. Many times ☐
b. Never ☐
c. Once or twice ☐

QUESTION 6

YOU TRY TO PUT YOURSELF INTO OTHER PEOPLE'S SHOES AND IMAGINE HOW THEY MUST BE FEELING.

a. True ☐
b. False ☐
c. Don't understand ☐

QUESTION 7

WHAT DO YOU MOST FEAR?

a. Not sure ☐
b. Loss ☐
c. Loneliness ☐

QUESTION 8

WHO DO YOU VALUE MOST?

a. A good teacher ☐
b. A skilled warrior ☐
c. A superb athlete ☐

ADD UP YOUR SCORES AND KEEP A NOTE OF YOUR TOTAL.

Design a Planet

What sort of planet would you create if you had the power? Use this template to draw your own planet. Use your stickers to complete the picture and then complete the Visitors' Guide.

20

Visitors' Guide

Name:

Terrain:

Atmosphere:

Population:

Native species:

Main industry:

Affiliation:

Largest city:

Political system:

Ruler:

Defence systems:

Darth Maul has landed on Tatooine. He sends probe droids to search for the missing Naboo ship. It is only a matter of time before he discovers the Queen!

Qui-Gon realises that the Force is unusually strong with Anakin. His midi-chlorian count is even higher than that of Master Yoda. Qui-Gon makes an arrangement with Watto. If Anakin wins, Qui-Gon will free him and take him to Coruscant.

Everyone gathers nervously at Mos Espa arena to watch the race. Anakin is close behind his main rival, a cheating Dug called Sebulba. Other Podracers crash and burn, but the little slave boy is a magnificent pilot. At last, on a tight corner, Anakin dives to the inside and takes the lead. Sebulba is furious!

He cheats, but his plan backfires and he crashes. Anakin races over the finish line – he has won!

Qui-Gon takes the new parts to the ship and then returns to fetch Anakin. He tells the boy that he wants to train him as a Jedi. Anakin is delighted, and says a loving goodbye to his mother.

The ship is about to leave Tatooine when Darth Maul finds it. He and Qui-Gon have a deadly duel, and Darth Maul is defeated. The ship speeds away, but the Jedi are worried.

During the journey to Coruscant, Padmé gets to know Anakin better. She tells him that the Queen is worried about her people.

Anakin gives her a pendant that he made for her.

On Coruscant, a special meeting of the Senate has been called, but Naboo's Senator Palpatine is worried. The Republic is full of greedy, corrupt senators. He persuades Queen Amidala to call for a Vote of No Confidence in Supreme Chancellor Valorum.

Qui-Gon tells members of the Jedi Council he thinks he was attacked by a Sith Lord. They are shocked and worried. They order Qui-Gon to stay with the Queen and protect her.

Qui-Gon tells them about Anakin and says that he may be the Chosen One mentioned in ancient prophecy. He asks the Council to test the boy, as he wants him to be trained as a Jedi.

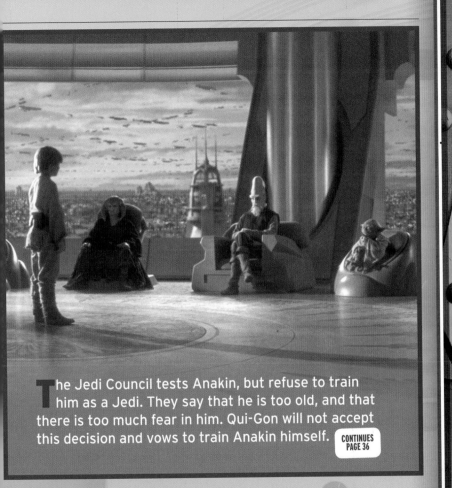

The Jedi Council tests Anakin, but refuse to train him as a Jedi. They say that he is too old, and that there is too much fear in him. Qui-Gon will not accept this decision and vows to train Anakin himself.

CONTINUES PAGE 36

qui-gon jinn

obi-wan kenobi

anakin skywalker

padmé amidala

WHICH WEAPON?

MACE WINDU

DARTH MAUL

Can you match these warriors to their weapons?

Locate the correct stickers and put them in the right places.

BATTLE DROID

DARTH SIDIOUS

TEST YOUR JEDI SKILLS

QUESTION 1

HOW MANY CLOSE FRIENDS DO YOU HAVE?

a. 1-2 ☐
b. 3-4 ☐
c. More than 5 ☐

QUESTION 2

HOW DO YOU REACT WHEN YOU FEEL AFRAID?

a. Run away ☐
b. Cry but face your fear ☐
c. Hide your fear under a mask ☐

QUESTION 3

WHICH POSITION WOULD YOU PLAY IN A GAME OF ROUNDERS?

a. Fielder ☐
b. Batter ☐
c. Bowler ☐

QUESTION 4

HOW OLD WERE YOU IN YOUR EARLIEST MEMORY?

a. Less than a year ☐
b. Less than five years ☐
c. Five years or more ☐

[HIGH PRIORITY]

JEDI COUNCIL
APPROVED!

TOP SECRET

JUSTICE

EYES ONLY

TIE SQUADRON

24-34 :: Congratulations! You have passed our tests – we believe that you are ready to train as a Jedi.

11-23 :: You are not ready to train as a Jedi, but if you work hard you have the potential to be successful.

0-10 :: The dark side must have been working against you! Have another go, we are sure you will do better!

QUESTION 5

HAVE YOU EVER SENSED THAT A PLACE 'FELT' HAPPY OR SAD?

a. Yes	☐
b. No	☐
c. Don't understand the question	☐

QUESTION 6

LAST TIME YOU HAD AN INJURY THAT BLED:

a. You fainted with the pain	☐
b. You didn't notice	☐
c. You treated it and then forgot about it	☐

QUESTION 7

A BAD TEMPER IS:

a. Loss of control	☐
b. A healthy display of emotions	☐
c. A sign of mental illness	☐

QUESTION 8

HOW MANY OF THESE FACTS DO YOU KNOW ABOUT YOUR BEST FRIEND?

a. Middle name	☐
b. Place of birth	☐
c. Favourite colour	☐

CHECK YOUR SCORE ON PAGE 52 [?]

33

Use the grid to copy this picture of a loyal friend of the Jedi. Then fill in his name below your drawing.

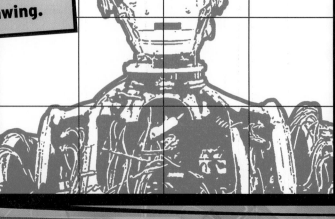

THE PHANTOM menace

The Queen decides that while a new Supreme Chancellor is elected, she will return to Naboo. She leaves with the Jedi, Anakin, Jar Jar and her faithful handmaidens and soldiers.

The Queen knows that she is heading for war. She is determined to rid her planet of the invasion. But Darth Sidious learns of their plans and sends Darth Maul to Naboo!

36

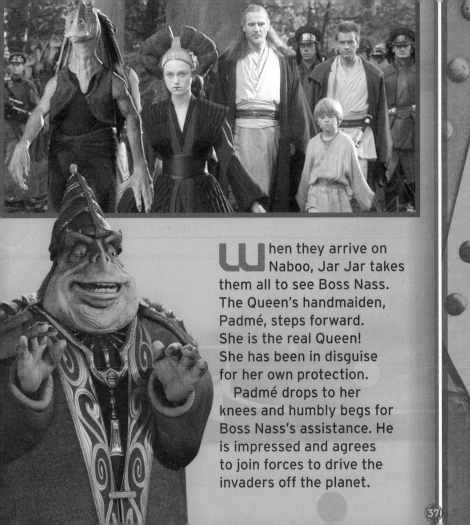

When they arrive on Naboo, Jar Jar takes them all to see Boss Nass. The Queen's handmaiden, Padmé, steps forward. She is the real Queen! She has been in disguise for her own protection.

Padmé drops to her knees and humbly begs for Boss Nass's assistance. He is impressed and agrees to join forces to drive the invaders off the planet.

The Gungans draw the droid army away from Theed with a decoy battle. At the same time, Padmé leads a strike team into the palace hangar.

Anakin hides inside a Naboo starfighter while the Naboo pilots take off to attack the droid control ship. Darth Maul

appears and duels with the Jedi, while battle droids attack the strike team.

he Jedi cannot defend Padmé, but Anakin fires lasers at the battle droids and Padmé is safe. She and her team enter the palace and capture Gunray. Meanwhile, Anakin cannot control the starfighter. It blasts into space – with him at the helm!

The Gungans are battling well, but there are simply too many droids to defeat. The fighters must succeed in disabling the droid control ship!

As the battle rages on above them, the Jedi are still duelling the vicious Darth Maul. Suddenly he runs his lightsaber through Qui-Gon! Obi-Wan destroys Darth Maul, but he cannot save his Master. Before he dies, Qui-Gon makes Obi-Wan swear to train Anakin as a Jedi.

evading attack, Anakin flies the fighter straight into the space station hangar. He fires two torpedoes into the reactor and the ship begins to explode.

The droids on the planet's surface lose power – the battle has been won!

The Jedi know that the mysterious warrior was a Sith. They also know that another Sith must exist somewhere. They can sense that troubled times lie ahead.

WORD SCRAMBLE

CAN YOU UNTANGLE THESE ANAGRAMS
TO DISCOVER SOME FAMOUS NAMES?

1. A DRUM HALT

2. A TEN RUN GUY

3. WHY AS ELK SMIRK

4. SEA BULB

5. A PANEL PIT

SPOT THE ROYAL DIFFERENCE

There are eight differences between these pictures of the queen. Can you find them all? Give yourself a gold star if you succeed.

45

[MISSION PLANNER]

Do you have a mission to organise?
Use this exclusive mission planner
to ensure that nothing is forgotten.
Then add stickers to ensure that the
document remains secret.

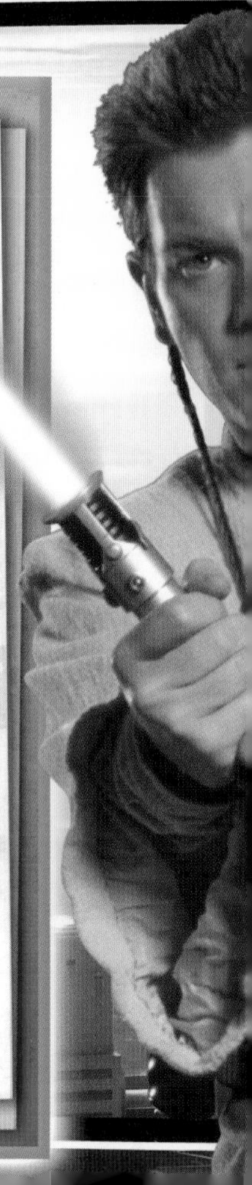

MISSION NAME: _____

PURPOSE: _____

TEAM LEADER: _____

STRIKE TEAM: _____

DESTINATION: _____

DATE: _____

TIME: _____

TRANSPORT: _____

WEAPONS: _____

TARGET: _____

DROIDS: _____

SUPPLIES: _____

HISTORY HIJACK

It's time to brush up your galactic history! This test paper has been censored - can you figure out where the deleted words belong?

SPACECRAFT

BATTLESHIP

THE TRADE FEDERATION

PODRACE

QUEEN AMIDALA

DARTH SIDIOUS

JAR JAR BINKS

SPEEDER BIKE

THE TRADE FEDERATION

REFUEL

BOSS NASS

THE ROYAL PALACE

1. _____ blockaded Naboo.

2. Nute Gunray was acting under the orders of _____

3. Queen Amidala was captured in _____ .

4. Two Jedi travelled to _____ _____ to negotiate peace.

5. Qui-Gon Jinn saved the life of _____ .

6. _____ loaned the Jedi a bongo.

7. The Jedi rescued _____ in Theed.

8. The Naboo _____ stopped on Tatooine to _____ .

9. A slave boy called Anakin won a dangerous _____ .

10. Darth Maul scoured the planet on his _____ .

TRUE OR FALSE

1	ANAKIN DUELLED AGAINST DARTH MAUL.	TRUE	FALSE
2	SHMI SKYWALKER WAS A ROYAL PRINCESS.	TRUE	FALSE
3	WATTO WAS A TOYDARIAN.	TRUE	FALSE
4	ANAKIN CREATED R2-D2.	TRUE	FALSE
5	OBI-WAN KENOBI DISCOVERED ANAKIN ON TATOOINE.	TRUE	FALSE

How much can you remember of Anakin's earliest adventures in space? Decide whether these statements are true or false and then check your answers. If you score more than 8/10, award yourself a gold star sticker.

6 QUEEN AMIDALA DISGUISED HERSELF AS A HANDMAIDEN. TRUE FALSE

7 NUTE GUNRAY WAS A SITH LORD. TRUE FALSE

8 THE TRADE FEDERATION BLOCKADED NABOO. TRUE FALSE

9 BOSS NASS WAS A GUNGAN. TRUE FALSE

10 JAR JAR BINKS GREW UP IN THE UNDERWATER CITY OF THEED. TRUE FALSE

ANSWERS

PAGES 10-11

C	I	N	C	I	D	U	I	E	T	U	E	R	O	S
I	Q	T	A	T	O	O	I	N	E	B	L	A	N	A
D	A	T	I	R	I	T	V	A	E	A	F	A	O	E
I	F	A	C	I	P	T	E	B	T	V	E	L	I	M
S	Q	T	U	E	R	A	I	O	O	Q	U	A	S	S
G	W	N	R	I	L	W	O	O	U	N	U	T	A	O
U	L	A	Q	O	D	D	U	I	E	T	G	O	V	R
I	O	C	Y	N	R	D	E	R	O	E	A	O	N	Y
S	P	S	T	Z	O	A	R	E	P	U	B	L	I	C
E	Q	U	U	L	I	E	I	E	R	S	E	D	E	E
L	E	R	B	P	D	O	U	T	R	I	L	I	Q	H
I	M	O	Q	E	S	E	V	A	L	S	L	A	A	P
Q	U	C	E	P	S	U	S	N	E	S	S	I	B	O
U	A	P	A	Q	O	N	S	E	L	T	T	A	B	R
L	S	N	A	G	N	U	G	S	I	L	L	A	C	P

PAGES 18-19

Question	a	b	c
1	2	1	0
2	1 point for each ability		
3	2	1	0
4	0	1	2
5	2	0	1
6	2	0	1
7	2	0	1
8	2	0	1

PAGES 30-31

MACE WINDU

DARTH MAUL

BATTLE DROID

DARTH SIDIOUS

PAGES 32-33

Question	a	b	c
1	2	1	0
2	1	2	0
3	2	1	0
4	2	0	1
5	2	0	1
6	1	0	2
7	2	0	1
8	1 point for each fact		

PAGES 34-35

C-3PO

PAGES 42-43

1. DARTH MAUL // 2. NUTE GUNRAY // 3. SHMI SKYWALKER // 4. SEBULBA // 5. PALPATINE

PAGES 44-45

PAGES 50-51

1. FALSE
2. FALSE
3. TRUE
4. FALSE
5. FALSE
6. TRUE
7. FALSE
8. TRUE
9. TRUE
10. FALSE

PAGES 48-49

1. The Trade Federation blockaded Naboo.
2. Nute Gunray was acting under the orders of Darth Sidious.
3. Queen Amidala was captured in the royal palace.
4. Two Jedi travelled to the Trade Federation battleship to negotiate peace.
5. Qui-Gon Jinn saved the life of Jar Jar Binks.
6. Boss Nass loaned the Jedi a bongo.
7. The Jedi rescued Queen Amidala in Theed.
8. The Naboo spacecraft stopped on Tatooine to refuel.
9. A slave boy called Anakin won a dangerous Podrace.
10. Darth Maul scoured the planet on his speeder bike.